Write on Track

SOURCEBOOK

Practice Workshops, Minilessons, and Daily Sentences

. . . a resource of student workshops, minilessons, and activities to accompany

Write on Track

WRITE SOURCE®

GREAT SOURCE EDUCATION GROUP
a Houghton Mifflin Company
Wilmington, Massachusetts

A Few Words About the SourceBook

Before you begin . . .

You need to know that your SourceBook should be used with the *Write on Track* handbook, which provides information, examples, and models. The SourceBook offers you opportunities to practice the editing and proofreading skills presented in the handbook. SourceBook activities include Practice Workshops, Minilessons, and MUG Shot Sentences.

Practice Workshops

The Practice Workshops cover what you need to know to become a better writer and proofreader. You will find that the workshop topics appear in the same order in the SourceBook as they do in the Proofreader's Guide in the *Write on Track* handbook.

Minilessons

Each Minilesson covers an important writing or learning idea from the handbook. Most minilessons can be done on your own or with a partner.

Daily MUG Shot Sentences

The MUG Shot Sentences review basic mechanics, usage, and grammar skills. Focused Sentences help you work on one skill at a time. The Proofreading Sentences offer several different sentence problems for you to correct.

Authors: Pat Sebranek and Dave Kemper

Trademarks and trade names are shown in this book strictly for illustrative purposes and are the property of their respective owners. The authors' references herein should not be regarded as affecting their validity.

Printed in the United States of America

International Standard Book Number: 0-669-43280-6

18 19 20 21 22 -DBH- 08 07 06 05

TABLE OF CONTENTS

1 Practice Workshops

Using the Right Word

Understanding Sentences

Understanding Our Language

2
Minilessons

Using Punctuation

Checking Mechanics

Understanding Sentences

Understanding Our Language

3 MUG Shot Sentences

Focused Sentences

Proofreading Sentences

1

Practice Workshops

The activities in this section cover the basic language, editing, and proofreading skills you need to become a better writer.

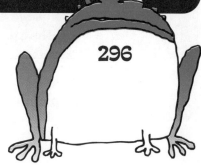

Using Periods

A **period** is just a little dot, but it has a lot of important uses. For one thing, a period is used at the end of a sentence that makes a statement.

Statements
Frogs begin their life in the water.
Later, they live on land.
Frogs are amphibians.

A period is also used at the end of a request.

Requests
Please look up "amphibian" in the dictionary.
Find out what the word means.

---

1 Put an **S** in front of each statement, and an **R** in front of each request. End each sentence with a period.

Example: __S__ Most frogs are expert swimmers.

__S__ 1. Frogs get much of their power from their strong back legs

__R__ 2. Do the frog kick next time you are in the water

__R__ 3. Draw both legs up to your side

__R__ 4. Then push them straight back

__S__ 5. You will move forward just as a frog does _RIGHT_

__S__ 6. You might enjoy swimming this way

__S__ 7. Frogs wouldn't swim in any other way

2 The following paragraph has seven sentences in it. Find the seven sentences and put a capital letter at the beginning of each one and a period at the end of each one.

Example: $\overset{S}{\cancel{s}}$ome frogs have homes that are high

off the ground $\underset{\bullet}{.}$ $\overset{T}{\cancel{t}}$hese frogs live in trees $\bullet$

$\overset{T}{\cancel{t}}$ree frogs like leafy homes $\bullet$ $\overset{M}{m}$any tree frogs are

green like the leaves $\bullet$ $\overset{N}{n}$ot all of them are green $\underset{\circ}{.}$ $\overset{S}{\cancel{s}}$ome

are yellow, red, or orange $\underset{.}{.}$ $\overset{O}{\cancel{o}}$thers have stripes and spots $\circ$

$\overset{T}{\cancel{t}}$ree frogs live in all parts of the world $\underset{\bullet}{.}$ $\overset{Y}{y}$ou may have

some in your neighborhood $\bullet$

NEXT STOP Write two sentences. In the first one, state something that a frog can do. In the second one, tell a friend to do something that a frog does.

1. *Statement*

_____

_____

_____

2. *Request*

_____

_____

_____

U.P.S. 296

Using Periods

Put a **period** after an initial in a person's name, and after an abbreviation. Also use a period as a decimal point in numbers.

Carl B. Picklefoot	M. Jennifer Jump
Mr. Picklefoot	Foster Ave.
$1.25	3.5 pounds

1   **Put periods after the initials in Samantha's name. Then write your name in each of the same ways.**

Samantha R.   _Fahad H._

Samantha J. Rowe   _Fahad A. Hasnain_

S. J. Rowe   _F. A. Hasnain_

S. J. R.   _F. A. H._

2   **Put periods after the abbreviations in these sentences.**

1. Where does Mr. Brown live?

2. He used to live on W. Water St., but now he has moved.

3. His new home is on E. Carver Ave., next door to Ms. Trout.

4. Ms. Trout is a dentist, so she is also Dr. Trout.

5. One of Mr. Brown's other neighbors is Lt. O'Malley, a police officer.

6. Many of the homes on E. Carver Ave. were built by J. J. Builders.

Put periods where they belong in the sentences below. (There are 11 periods missing.)

Example: Mr. Henry J. Picklefoot went to E. Lancaster to visit his cousin Ms. Mary W. Bristle.

Ms. Bristle works at a movie theater in E. Lancaster. The theater is on W. Broad St., just past J. J. Pollacco's Pizza Palace. While Ms. Bristle was working, Mr. Picklefoot went to three movies. Each one cost $7.00. The next day, Mr. Picklefoot decided to go back home to W. Lancaster. He had seen enough movies.

Write two names that have abbreviations or initials and two numbers with decimal points. Then write two sentences using these names and numbers.

Names   *Numbers with Decimal Points*

_____   _____

_____   _____

Sentences

✔ _____

_____

✔ _____

_____

Punctuating Sentences

296, 303, 304

✱ You use a **question mark** after a question.

Do you want broccoli for supper?

✱ An **exclamation point** follows a word or sentence that shows strong feeling.

Wow! That's a great idea!

✱ A **period** follows a statement or a request.

I'm not sure I believe you. Say that again.

1 Put a period, a question mark, or an exclamation point at the end of each of these sentences.

1. What's so good about broccoli __?__

2. Broccoli is rich in vitamins __.__

3. It tastes great __!__

4. It has a pretty green color __.__

5. The home gardener finds it easy to grow __.__

6. Why doesn't everyone eat broccoli __?__

7. I like it with cheese sauce __.__

8. Who likes it raw __?__

9. I do __!__ I do __!__

10. Broccoli is definitely my favorite vegetable __!__

2 Put a question mark, an exclamation point, or a period at the end of each sentence in this paragraph.

My favorite vegetable is carrots! They're so sweet. Do you know how my little brother eats carrots? He puts them in rolls and eats them like hot dogs. It's gross! What is your favorite vegetable? Do you like carrots, too?

NEXT STOP Write three sentences about one of the vegetables listed below. One sentence should make a statement or request, another sentence should ask a question, and the third one should express strong feeling.

eggplant   cabbage   asparagus   squash   corn

1. Statement

My mom likes cabbage.

2. Question

Do you like cabbage?

3. Exclamation

I hate cabbage!

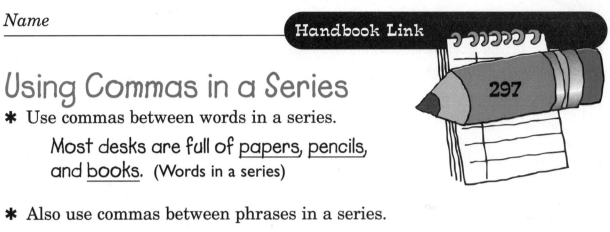

Using Commas in a Series

✻ Use commas between words in a series.

   Most desks are full of <u>papers</u>, <u>pencils</u>, and <u>books</u>. (Words in a series)

✻ Also use commas between phrases in a series.

   My dad uses <u>solar calculators</u>, <u>felt-tip pens</u>, and <u>Post-it Notes</u>. (Phrases in a series)

1 In each sentence, put commas between the words and phrases in the series.

1. My mom's desk is covered with letters, bills, and pictures.

2. Paper clips, safety pins, and thumbtacks are in a jar.

3. She keeps rulers, scissors, and a plant on the shelf.

4. The top drawer holds stickers, rubber bands, two checkbooks, and three notepads.

5. The bottom drawer contains spiral notebooks, file folders, and old letters.

6. She keeps pencils, pens, and markers in a can that I made in school.

7. A dictionary, a world atlas, and two telephone directories are placed on another shelf.

Make a list of things you have in your desk.

_____   _____

_____   _____

_____   _____

_____   _____

_____   _____

_____   _____

_____   _____

Now write three sentences about the things in your desk. Your sentences should include words or phrases in a series.

1. _____

_____

_____

2. _____

_____

_____

3. _____

_____

_____

Using Commas in Addresses and Dates

1 Write the names, addresses, and birth dates (including the year) for two of your classmates or friends. Make sure to use commas correctly.

Name _____

Address _____

City and State _____

Birth Date _____

Name _____

Address _____

City and State _____

Birth Date _____

 **2** Complete each invitation below using the names and addresses from the first page in this activity. (Feel free to decorate the invitations.)

SURPRISE PARTY

Please come to a surprise party for

_____

Date: _____

Time: _____

Address: _____

_____

Neighborhood Picnic

Please join _____

for an afternoon of fun.

Address: _____

_____

Date: _____

Time: _____

Using Quotation Marks in Dialogue

* One way to show what people say to each other is to use speech balloons. They are fun, but they take up a lot of room.

> I tried to call you, but your line was busy.

> I'm not surprised. My sister was on the phone all night.

* Another way to show what people say is to use **quotation marks**. The quotation marks set off the exact words of the speaker.

> Tom said,"I tried to call you, but your line was busy."

> "I'm not surprised. My sister was on the phone all night," Jerry answered.

1 Read the words in the speech balloons below. Then in the sentences that follow, put quotation marks before and after the exact words that Tom and Jerry said.

> I wanted to ask if you could sleep over Saturday night.

> I hope I can. I'll ask my mom.

Tom said, I wanted to ask if you could sleep over Saturday night.

I hope I can. I'll ask my mom, said Jerry.

2 Read the speech balloons that follow. Then in the space below write what Tom and Jerry said, using quotation marks correctly in your sentences.

My dad and I are going to set up the tent in the yard.

Great! I'll bring my sleeping bag.

Tom said, _____

_____

_____

Jerry replied, _____

_____

_____

NEXT STOP It's the next day. Tom and Jerry see each other again. Now you decide what they say. Make sure to use quotation marks correctly.

_____

_____

_____

_____

Name _____

Using Quotation Marks in Dialogue

302

When you write **dialogue**, you can identify the speaker at the beginning of the sentence, at the end of the sentence, or in the middle of the sentence.

✱ Here's how to use commas and quotation marks when the speaker is identified at the **beginning** of the sentence:

Carla said, "I'm going to camp this summer."

✱ When the speaker is identified at the **end** of the sentence, use commas and quotation marks like this:

"Late at night, we tell ghost stories," said Camy.

✱ When the speaker is identified in the **middle** of the sentence, commas and quotation marks are used like this:

"Camp starts July 5," Carla said, "and we stay for two weeks."

1

Add commas and quotation marks where they are needed in the following sentences. The speaker is identified at the beginning of the sentence.

1. Camy said I'm going, too.

2. Josh said Won't you miss your parents?

3. Carla answered Yes, but we'll still have fun.

4. Josh asked What are you going to bring?

5. Carla said I'm bringing a lot of shorts and T-shirts.

 **Add commas and quotation marks in the sentences below. The speaker is identified at the end of the sentence.**

1. The ghost stories always scare me a little Camy said.

2. I'd be scared, too said Josh.

3. Aw, they're only fake stories! said Carla.

 **Add commas and quotation marks in the following sentences. The speaker is identified in the middle of the sentence.**

1. This summer said Carla I'm going to learn to dive.

2. I can dive Camy said but not headfirst.

3. If it's not headfirst said Josh it's not a dive.

4. If it's belly first said Josh it's a belly flop!

 **Write one more thing talked about between two of the campers. Use commas and quotation marks correctly to punctuate your dialogue.**

_____

_____

_____

_____

Reviewing Capitalization

1 Add capital letters in each of the following paragraphs. Also answer the question after each paragraph. (The first two capital letters have been added.)

Rub It Out

$\overset{I}{\cancel{i}}$n 1770, an $\overset{E}{\cancel{e}}$nglishman named joseph priestley was traveling in south america. he gathered some of the juice coming from the trees. he found that it would rub out pencil marks. he called it rubber.

What are three things that are made of rubber?

_____   _____   _____

Blast It

in sweden, a man named alfred nobel invented a safe blasting material he called dynamite. miners often use dynamite. money he earned from the invention now goes to people who win the nobel prize.

Why do miners use dynamite?

_____

_____

Here are two more paragraphs to capitalize. Also answer the question at the end of each paragraph.

Weave It

long ago, empress si ling-chi was sipping tea in china. a caterpillar cocoon fell into her cup. she unwound the cocoon and said, "it's made of a long silk thread. what will happen if I have it woven into cloth?" that's how chinese silk was discovered.

What are three things that are made of silk?

_____   _____   _____

Wipe It Off

an american woman, mary anderson, had a good idea in 1903. "aha!" she thought. "if you push a rubber blade across a windshield, you can wipe away rain and snow." what do we call her invention today?

Answer: _____

Writing Numbers

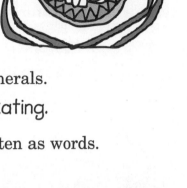

✳ Numbers from one to nine are usually written as words.

> Gymnast Mary Lou Retton won <u>five</u> Olympic medals in one year.

✳ Numbers larger than 10 are usually written as numerals.

> The U.S. has won <u>42</u> world titles in figure skating.

TIP: Numbers at the beginning of sentences are written as words.

1 **Follow the directions for each sentence. Make sure to write your numbers correctly.**

1. Write a sentence telling how old you are.

   _____

2. Write a sentence using a very large number.

   _____

3. Write a sentence about the number of doors in your classroom.

   _____

4. Write a sentence naming an amount of money.

   _____

5. Write a sentence telling how many students are wearing tennis shoes in your class.

   _____

Using Abbreviations

When you shorten a word or phrase, you make an **abbreviation**. Most abbreviations begin with a capital letter and end with a period.

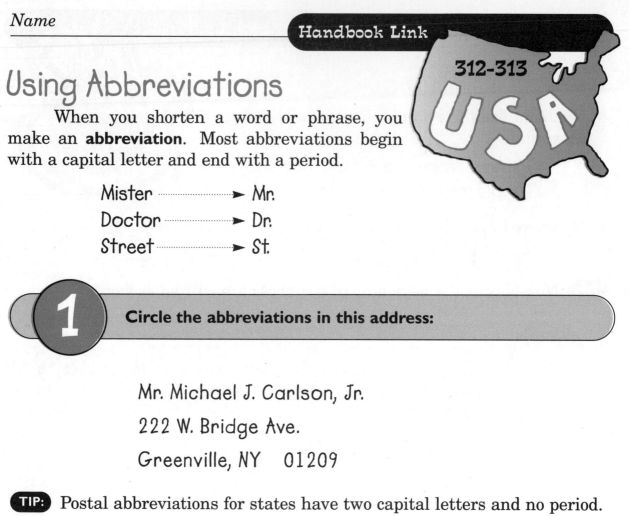

312-313

Mister ━━━━➤ Mr.

Doctor ━━━━➤ Dr.

Street ━━━━➤ St.

1 **Circle the abbreviations in this address:**

Mr. Michael J. Carlson, Jr.

222 W. Bridge Ave.

Greenville, NY   01209

TIP: Postal abbreviations for states have two capital letters and no period.

Massachusetts ━━━━━➤ MA

 NEXT STOP **Write your name and address here. Use at least two abbreviations.**

_____
(name)

_____
(street)

_____
(city & state)

Subject of a Sentence

325

✱ Every sentence has a subject. The **subject** of a sentence names something or someone.

>   My old friend jumped over the candlestick.
>   (*My old friend* is the complete subject.)

✱ The **simple subject** is the main word in the subject.

>   My old friend jumped over the candlestick.
>   (*Friend* is the simple subject.)

✱ A **compound subject** is made up of two or more simple subjects.

>   Jack and Jill jumped over the candlestick.
>   (*Jack* and *Jill* is the compound subject.)

1

Draw a line under the complete subject. Circle the simple subject.

Examples: A few little seeds fell to the ground.

1. An enormous beanstalk grew up and up.

2. Brave Jack climbed the beanstalk.

3. A huge castle rose up out of the clouds.

4. The ugly giant roared, "Fee, fie, fo, fum!"

5. The giant's wife saved Jack.

6. An old clock protected Jack from the giant.

7. Frightened little Jack stayed very still.

Draw a line under the complete subject in each sentence below. Write an S in the blank if the main part of the subject is simple or a C if the main part is compound.

Example: __C__ The giant and his wife ate dinner.

_____ 1. The ugly giant called for his magic goose.

_____ 2. The magic goose laid golden eggs.

_____ 3. The giant and the goose slept.

_____ 4. Jack snatched the goose.

_____ 5. The bold boy climbed down the beanstalk.

_____ 6. The surprised giant chased him.

_____ 7. Jack's mother chopped down the beanstalk.

_____ 8. Jack and his mother lived happily ever after.

NEXT STOP **Write three sentences about a favorite fairy tale. Underline the complete subject in each sentence you write.**

1. _____

_____

2. _____

_____

3. _____

_____

Name _____

Handbook Link

326

Predicate of a Sentence

✱ The **predicate** (verb) part of a sentence tells what the subject is or does.

> Maya <u>writes stories on her computer</u>.
>
> (*Writes stories on her computer* is the complete predicate.)

✱ The **simple predicate** is the main word in the predicate.

> Maya (writes) stories on her computer.
>
> (*Writes* is the simple predicate.)

✱ A **compound predicate** is made up of two or more simple predicates.

> Maya (writes) stories and (plays) music on her computer.
>
> (*Writes* and *plays* is the compound predicate.)

1 **Draw two lines under the complete predicate. Circle the simple predicate, or verb.**

Example: Maya (thinks) <u>of good stories</u>.

1. Maya writes about a magic keyboard.

2. The keyboard creates 100-page stories overnight.

3. Everybody loves the stories.

4. She wins dozens of prizes.

5. She becomes a great author.

6. Maya wants a magic keyboard like this.

Understanding Sentences **51**

Draw two lines under the complete predicate in each sentence below. Write an S in the blank if the main part of the predicate is simple or a C if the main part is compound.

Example: ___C___ Maya <u>writes and composes music</u>.

_____ 1. Maya composes music on her computer.

_____ 2. She plays the melody and sings the words.

_____ 3. Maya's friends join her.

_____ 4. They sing old songs and make up new ones.

_____ 5. Maya's dog sings, too.

_____ 6. The dog barks and howls.

_____ 7. Maya's mother listens to the singing.

_____ 8. She smiles and shakes her head.

_____ 9. She joins in the fun.

_____ 10. Everyone has a good time.

Complete each thought below. Underline the complete predicate in your sentences.

The best computer game _____

_____.

My friends and I _____

_____.

Name _____

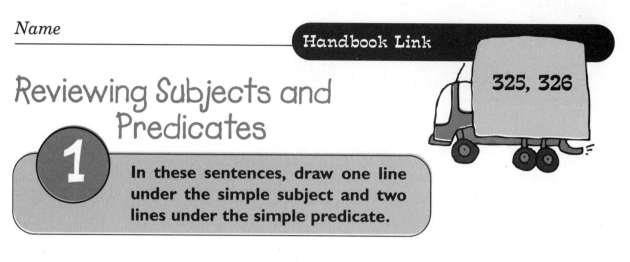

Reviewing Subjects and Predicates

1 In these sentences, draw one line under the simple subject and two lines under the simple predicate.

Example: <u>Betty Bodette</u> <u><u>drives</u></u> a red convertible.

1. My father drives a truck.

2. The truck belongs to a landscaping company.

3. I ride with my father sometimes.

4. My big sister comes, too.

5. We help my father.

6. He treats us to lunch at noon.

2 Put a check in the subject box if the sentence below has a compound subject. Put a check in the predicate box if the sentence has a compound predicate.

Example: Betty and her sister drive to the mall.

1. Betty buys a sundae and goes to the movies.
2. Betty and her sister like funny movies.
3. Her brother skateboards and plays video games.
4. He and his friends like to ride in the convertible.
5. They ride to the mall and buy ice cream cones.

COMPOUND	
Subject	Predicate
✔	

Understanding Sentences **53**

3 Change each sentence so it has a compound subject. You will also have to change the predicate so that it agrees, or makes sense, with the new subject.

Example: Jeff walks to school.

Jeff and his friend walk to school.

1. Caroline rides on the bus.

_____

2. Mrs. Hodorowski likes to take the train.

_____

3. I walk with my friend Maria.

_____

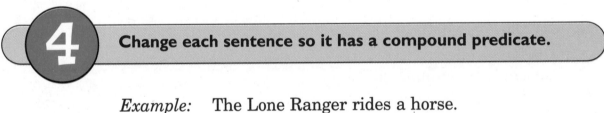

4 Change each sentence so it has a compound predicate.

Example: The Lone Ranger rides a horse.

The Lone Ranger rides a horse and

shoots silver bullets.

1. Mary Poppins flies with her umbrella.

_____

_____

2. Superman soars over the city.

_____

_____

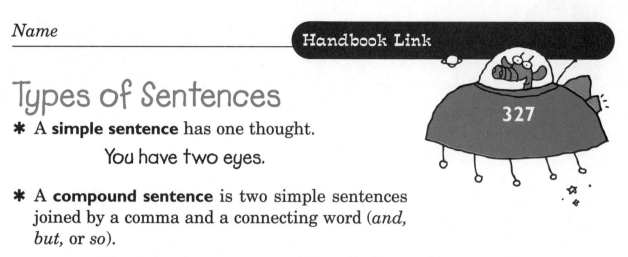

Handbook Link

327

Types of Sentences

✳ A **simple sentence** has one thought.

> You have two eyes.

✳ A **compound sentence** is two simple sentences joined by a comma and a connecting word (*and, but,* or *so*).

> You have two eyes, <u>and</u> they both see the same thing.

1

Carefully read each of the following sentences. Write an S in the blank for each simple sentence and a C for each compound sentence.

Examples: __S__ Miss Filbert loves science.

__C__ She talked about eyesight, and then she did an experiment.

_____ 1. Miss Filbert threw a ball to Peter, and he threw it back to her.

_____ 2. She caught the ball.

_____ 3. Then she put on an eye patch.

_____ 4. Peter threw the ball again.

_____ 5. Miss Filbert reached out to catch the ball, but she missed it.

_____ 6. Miss Filbert made an important point.

_____ 7. Two eyes help us see in 3-D, and they help us catch a ball.

2 Combine each set of simple sentences to make a compound sentence.

Example: Some eyes are blue. Some eyes are brown.
Some eyes are blue, and some eyes are brown.

1. A horse has two eyes. They are on the sides of its head.

_____

_____

2. A human has simple eyes. A dragonfly has compound eyes.

_____

_____

3. Fish see underwater. Many of them see in color.

_____

_____

 Write one simple sentence and one compound sentence about your eyes.

Simple Sentence:

_____

_____

Compound Sentence:

_____

_____

327

Kinds of Sentences

✳ A **declarative sentence** makes a statement.

　　Michaelangelo was a sculptor.

✳ An **interrogative sentence** asks a question.

　　What does a sculptor do?

✳ An **imperative sentence** gives a command or makes a request.

　　Ask your teacher what a sculptor does.

✳ An **exclamatory sentence** shows strong emotion or surprise.

　　That's a great idea!

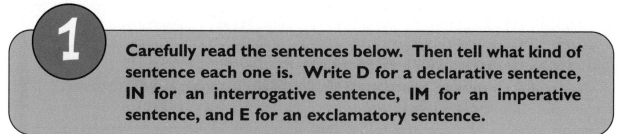

1　Carefully read the sentences below. Then tell what kind of sentence each one is. Write **D** for a declarative sentence, **IN** for an interrogative sentence, **IM** for an imperative sentence, and **E** for an exclamatory sentence.

Example: A sculptor makes figures in stone or clay. ___D___

1. Do you know any other sculptors? _____

2. Donatello was a sculptor. _____

3. I don't believe it! _____

4. Look it up if you don't believe me. _____

5. Michaelangelo studied Donatello's sculptures. _____

6. What was so great about Donatello? _____

**2** Turn each statement into a question. You may have to add, drop, or change the order of the words to make your new sentences.

Example: Michaelangelo lived in Italy.

Where did Michaelangelo live?

1. Michaelangelo lived about 500 years ago.

_____

2. Michaelangelo was a painter and a sculptor.

_____

3. Many artists copy Michaelangelo's works.

_____

Write four sentences about a famous person. Use the four kinds of sentences: declarative, interrogative, imperative, and exclamatory.

Declarative: _____

_____

Interrogative: _____

_____

Imperative: _____

_____

Exclamatory: _____

_____

Correcting Sentence Fragments

A complete sentence has a subject and a predicate. If either one or both of these are missing, you have a **sentence fragment**.

✷ In this sentence fragment, the subject is missing.

Fragment: Jumped off the diving board.

Corrected Sentence: Jeb jumped off the diving board.
                (A subject has been added.)

✷ In this sentence fragment, the subject and verb are missing.

Fragment: In the pool.

Corrected Sentence: Jenna and Jane swam in the pool.
                (A subject and verb have been added.)

1 Write a C in front of each complete sentence below, and write an F in front of each sentence fragment.

Example: ___F___ An excellent swimmer.

_____ 1. Herman is an excellent swimmer.

_____ 2. Breaststroke, Australian crawl, and backstroke.

_____ 3. He is teaching me how to swim.

_____ 4. I am leaving.

_____ 5. Not very fast.

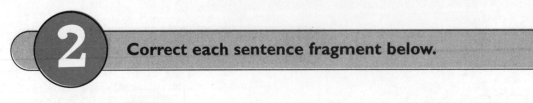

2 Correct each sentence fragment below.

Example: In the ocean

Missy McGee swims in the ocean.

1. Bought scuba equipment.

_____

_____

2. Below the surface.

_____

_____

3. Fish to left and right.

_____

_____

4. To chase away sharks.

_____

_____

5. Reached the boat.

_____

_____

NEXT STOP Read the fragments and your sentences to a partner. *Listen to the difference between a fragment and a complete sentence.*

Correcting Run-Ons

A **run-on sentence** happens when two or more sentences run together.

Run-on Sentence:

Mr. Wiggle's lawn mower needs repair he can't fix it.

Corrected Sentences:

Mr. Wiggle's lawn mower needs repair. He can't fix it.
                    (two sentences)

Mr. Wiggle's lawn mower needs repair, but he can't fix it.
                    (compound sentence)

1 | **Change each of these run-on sentences into two sentences.**

Example: He pulled the cord the engine didn't start.

He pulled the cord.   The engine didn't start.
_____

1. His grass was growing fast dandelions were popping up.

   _____

   _____

2. Mr. Wiggle borrowed our mower he has not returned it yet.

   _____

   _____

3. I hope he gives it back soon our grass is getting very long.

   _____

   _____

Correct each run-on sentence below by rewriting the run-on as a compound sentence.

Example: Mr. Wiggle tried to toast some bread it burned.

  Mr. Wiggle tried to toast some bread, but it burned.

1. The smoke set off a fire alarm the fire department came.

_____

_____

2. Mr. Wiggle was surprised to see the firefighters he told them what happened.

_____

_____

3. Mr. Wiggle threw out the toaster Mrs. Wiggle pulled it from the trash.

_____

_____

4. Mr. Wiggle bought a new toaster his wife fixed the old one.

_____

_____

5. Now the Wiggles have two toasters we're thinking of borrowing one.

_____

_____

Pair up with a classmate and check each other's compound sentences. Make sure your partner has placed a comma before the connecting word in each of his or her sentences.

72-73

Combining Sentences with a Key Word

One way to combine sentences is to move a **key word** from one sentence to the other.

Short Sentences: Lizzie plays basketball.
She is on the fifth-grade team.

Combined Sentence: Lizzie plays on the (fifth-grade) basketball team.
(The key word is circled.)

1

Circle the key word or words that were used to make a combined sentence. The first one has been done for you.

1. **Short sentences:**   Her team has new uniforms.

   They are blue and white.

   Combined sentence: Her team has new (blue and white) uniforms.

2. **Short sentences:**   Ms. Charleyhorse is the coach.

   She coaches basketball.

   Combined sentence: Ms. Charleyhorse is the basketball coach.

3. **Short sentences:**   The team goes to away games in a van.

   The van is brand-new.

   Combined sentence: The team goes to away games in a brand-new van.

4. **Short sentences:**   Laura cheers for Lizzie's team.

   She cheers loudly.

   Combined sentence: Laura cheers loudly for Lizzie's team.

Combine each set of sentences below by moving a key word from one sentence to the other.

1. Jesse loves to roller skate. He roller skates everyday.

   _____

   _____

2. Jesse sometimes uses his brother's roller skates. The roller skates are green.

   _____

   _____

3. Jesse likes to roller skate with his friends. He has five friends.

   _____

   _____

4. His friends are going to roller skate with him. They will roller skate tomorrow.

   _____

   _____

5. Everyone will practice for a race. The race will be long.

   _____

   _____

Write some interesting sentences about one of your favorite activities. Combine some of your ideas into longer sentences. (Use your own paper for your work.)

Combining Sentences with Words or Phrases in a Series

72-73 & 297

You can combine short sentences that tell different things about the same subject.

Short Sentences: George Washington Carver was curious. He was smart. He was hardworking.

Combined Sentence: George Washington Carver was <u>curious</u>, <u>smart</u>, and <u>hardworking</u>.

(The three words in a series tell different things about the subject.)

Combine these sentences using a series of words or phrases.

1. As a boy, George Washington Carver worked as a cook. He worked as a launderer. He worked as a janitor.

   _____

   _____

2. In the laboratory, Carver found new ways to use peanuts. He found new ways to use pecans. He found new ways to use sweet potatoes.

   _____

   _____

3. Carver made ink from sweet potatoes. He made flour from sweet potatoes. He made rubber from sweet potatoes.

   _____

   _____

Understanding Sentences **65**

2 Combine these sentences by using a key word from one sentence or by using words or phrases in a series.

1. Edison invented a lightbulb. He invented a phonograph. He invented a movie camera.

   _____

   _____

2. Thomas Edison asked questions that began with *why*. He asked questions that began with *how*.

   _____

   _____

3. Edison's inventions were easy to work. They were easy to keep in order. They were easy to fix.

   _____

   _____

4. He worked long hours and only took naps. The naps were short.

   _____

   _____

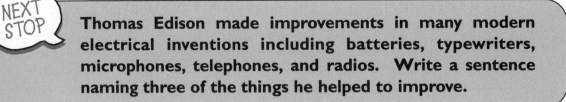

NEXT STOP   **Thomas Edison made improvements in many modern electrical inventions including batteries, typewriters, microphones, telephones, and radios. Write a sentence naming three of the things he helped to improve.**

_____

_____

_____

Combining Sentences with Compound Subjects & Verbs

Short Sentences: LaJoy went to the circus.
Kelly went to the circus.

**Combined
Sentence:** <u>LaJoy</u> and <u>Kelly</u> went to the circus.
(*LaJoy* and *Kelly* is a compound subject.)

* * * * * * * *

Short Sentences: LaJoy went to the circus.
She watched the clowns.

**Combined
Sentence:** LaJoy <u>went</u> to the circus and <u>watched</u> the clowns.
(*Went* and *watched* is a compound verb.)

1

Draw a line under the compound subject or the compound verb in each combined sentence.

1. **Short sentences:**   Tim likes the trapeze artists.
   Henry likes the trapeze artists.
   Combined sentence: Tim and Henry like the trapeze artists.

2. **Short sentences:**   High-wire performers ride bikes.
   They walk on their hands.
   Combined sentence: High-wire performers ride bikes and walk
   on their hands.

3. **Short sentences:**   Aerialists hang by their teeth.
   They twirl around.
   Combined sentence: Aerialists hang by their teeth and twirl around.

2 Combine these sentences using a compound subject or a compound verb.

1. Kelly munched popcorn. She gobbled peanuts.

   _____

   _____

2. Henry wanted cotton candy. His brother wanted cotton candy, too.

   _____

   _____

3. LaJoy bought balloons. Tim also bought balloons.

   _____

   _____

4. Kelly bought a clown wig. She stuck it on her head.

   _____

   _____

NEXT STOP Write two sentences about a circus. In one sentence, use a compound subject. In the other sentence, use a compound verb.

Compound Subject: _____

_____

Compound Verb: _____

_____

331

Helping Verbs

A **helping verb** comes before the main verb, and it helps state an action or show time.

Helping Verbs: has, have, had, will, could, do did, should, would, may, can

1 **Draw two lines under the helping verb and action verb in each sentence. (The first one has been done for you.)**

1. Parrots <u>can sleep</u> standing up.

2. Humpback whales do make a lot of noise.

3. Australians have named baby kangaroos "joeys."

4. A baby elephant will grow quickly.

5. Swans do eat plants, insects, and small fish.

2 **Write two sentences. Each sentence should contain one of the action verbs listed below, plus a helping verb. Draw two lines under the helping verb and the action verb.**

run   push   eat   called

Example: An elephant <u>can eat</u> a lot.

1. _____

_____

2. _____

_____

Reviewing Verbs

✻ There are two main types of verbs, **action verbs** and **linking verbs**.

I <u>fed</u> my dog. (*Fed* is an action verb.)

He <u>is</u> hungry. (*Is* is a linking verb.)

✻ Sometimes a **helping verb** is used with an action verb or a linking verb.

My dog <u>will eat</u> anything.

1 Draw two lines under the main verb in each sentence. Write an **A** in the blank if the verb shows action or an **L** if the verb links two words. The last two sentences contain helping verbs. For those sentences, underline the helping verbs, along with the main verbs.

Example: My dog <u>runs</u> fast. _____A_____

1. My dog acts like a person. _____

2. His name is Bob. _____

3. We are so happy with Bob. _____

4. He likes the kitchen. _____

5. My baby sister Nina loves Bob. _____

6. She sits in the kitchen with him. _____

7. Once she tasted Bob's dog food. _____

8. Nina should eat her own food! _____

9. Bob will be our friend forever. _____

332

Working with Verb Tense

✱ A verb in the **present tense** tells you that the action takes place now, or that it happens all the time.

A cricket <u>hops</u> across the lawn.

✱ A verb in the **past tense** means the action happened before, or in the past.

Yesterday a cricket <u>hopped</u> onto my leg.

1

Carefully read the following sentences. Write <u>present</u> in the blank if the underlined verb is in the present tense, or <u>past</u> if it is in the past tense.

Example:

Crickets <u>sing</u> by rubbing their wings together. ___present___

1. My grandfather <u>keeps</u> a singing cricket in a cage. _____

2. It <u>tells</u> the temperature. _____

3. On hot days it <u>chirps</u> fast. _____

4. I <u>heard</u> the cricket chirp a few minutes ago. _____

5. It <u>chirped</u> 50 times in 15 seconds. _____

6. I <u>tried</u> to chirp myself. _____

7. I <u>sounded</u> really stupid. _____

8. Chirping <u>gives</u> me a sore throat. _____

Each present tense verb is underlined. After each sentence, write the past tense of the verb. Then read the sentence with the new verb in it.

Example: Jiminy Cricket <u>meets</u> a beautiful fairy. _____met_____

Past Tense

1. He <u>helps</u> Pinocchio. _____

2. Jiminy <u>talks</u> about right from wrong. _____

3. Pinocchio <u>needs</u> Jiminy. _____

4. He <u>whistles</u> for Jiminy. _____

5. Jiminy Cricket <u>hops</u> to his side. _____

6. Then Jiminy <u>calls</u> for Geppetto. _____

7. Pinocchio <u>likes</u> Jiminy. _____

NEXT STOP Write two sentences about crickets. Use a present-tense verb in one sentence and a past-tense verb in the other one.

Present tense _____

_____

_____

Past tense _____

_____

_____

Working with Verb Tense

332

✻ Remember that a verb in the **present tense** tells you that the action takes place now, or happens all the time.

> It <u>snows</u>.
>
> I <u>make</u> a snowman.

✻ A verb in the **future tense** means the action will take place at a later time.

> The sun <u>will come</u> out.
>
> It <u>will melt</u> the snow.

1 After each sentence, check whether the underlined verb is in the present tense or in the future tense.

	PRESENT	FUTURE
Example: I <u>see</u> snow falling.	✓	
1. Snow <u>falls</u> softly and silently.		
2. It <u>covers</u> roads and roofs.		
3. I <u>hope</u> that it snows all night.		
4. Then they <u>will close</u> the schools.		
5. I <u>will have</u> to shovel snow.		
6. I <u>will clear</u> the walk.		
7. That <u>sounds</u> like too much work!		
8. I <u>want</u> the snow to stop.		

2 Draw two lines under the verb in each sentence. Write **present** in the blank if the verb is in the present tense and **future** if it is in the future tense.

Example: What <u><u>will melt</u></u> snow? _____*future*_____

1. Salt melts snow. _____

2. Dan's experiment will prove it. _____

3. Dan fills two cans with snow or ice. _____

4. He dumps salt on the snow in one can _____

5. He sets a timer for one hour. _____

6. Then he will look at the cans. _____

Change each of the following sentences to the future tense. Then write one more sentence about snow. Use the future tense in your new idea.

1. Snow falls.

_____

2. It clings to branches and twigs.

_____

3. Soon the world looks like a wedding cake.

_____

_____

4. _____

_____

Reviewing Verb Tense

The **tense** of a verb tells you if the action happened in the present, past, or future.

Present Tense:

Peter Piper <u>picks</u> a peck of pickled peppers.

Past Tense:

Peter Piper <u>picked</u> a peck of pickled peppers yesterday.

Future Tense:

Peter Piper <u>will pick</u> a peck of pickled peppers tomorrow.

Draw two lines under the verb in each of the following tongue twisters. Then in the blank space name the tense of the verb.

Example: A big black bug <u>bit</u> a big black bear. _____past_____

1. Three gray geese grazed in the green grass. _____

2. Teddy takes two turtles to Todd's house. _____

3. Barbara always burns the brown bread. _____

4. A flaw formed in the floor. _____

5. The dog will choose to chew the shoes. _____

6. She will sip a cup of coffee from a proper coffeepot. _____

7. He ran from the Indies to the Andes. _____

8. Carol collects colorful cups. _____

Present	Past	Future
run, runs	ran	will run
sells	sold	will sell
close	closed	will close
bubbles	bubbled	will bubble
throws	threw	will throw
watch	watched	will watch

Create your own tongue twisters by completing the sentences below. Select verbs from the list above.

Example: The ragged rascal _____ran_____ around the rocks.
    (past)

1. She _____ seashells down by the seashore.
    (past)

2. Don't _____ along the wrong lane!
    (present)

3. Clyde's Clothes Closet _____ for cleaning.
    (future)

4. Double bubble gum _____ double.
    (present)

5. Tom _____ Tim three thumbtacks.
    (past)

6. Two witches _____ two watches.
    (future)

Share your tongue twisters with a classmate. Write more examples to share. (Use your own paper.)

Using Regular Verbs

✳ You add -ed to regular verbs to form the past tense.

Willy and Milly <u>sailed</u> the boat last summer.

227 & 333

✳ You also add -ed to regular verbs when you use a helping verb like *has, have,* or *had.*

Willy <u>had sailed</u> for years.

✳ ✳ ✳ ✳ ✳ ✳ ✳ ✳ ✳

✳ If a regular verb ends in *e*, you just add *d* to form the past tense.

raise ·············► raise<u>d</u>

✳ If a one-syllable verb ends in a single consonant, you double the consonant and add -ed.

shop ·············► shopp<u>ed</u>

1   Write each of these regular verbs in the past tense.

1. hop _____

2. hope _____

3. name _____

4. tap _____

5. skip _____

6. raise _____

7. talk _____

8. hum _____

9. push _____

10. save _____

11. flip _____

12. splash _____

13. stop _____

14. giggle _____

15. lick _____

16. drip _____

2 In each set of sentences below, study the underlined verb in the first sentence. Then write the *-ed* form of the underlined verb to complete the second sentence.

Example: They <u>call</u> the boat the *Lilly*.

They ___called___ it the *Lilly* two years ago.

1. Milly <u>rows</u> out to the *Lilly*.

   Yesterday, Willy _____ out to the *Lilly*.

2. Milly <u>raises</u> the *Lilly's* sail.

   Last year, she _____ it every morning.

3. Milly and Willy <u>love</u> to sail the *Lilly*.

   Milly and Willy always have _____ to sail the *Lilly*.

4. Milly <u>drops</u> the anchor.

   On the day before, Milly _____ the anchor.

5. Willy <u>cleans</u> the *Lilly* once a week.

   He had _____ it two days ago.

 **Draw a picture including Milly, Willy, *and* Lilly.**

333

Using Singular and Plural Verbs

The subject of a sentence can be singular or plural. Notice how the verb *play* changes when the subject changes from singular to plural.

Caleb <u>plays</u> basketball at the park. (singular verb)

His friends <u>play</u> with him. (plural verb)

1 **Write the correct form of the verb in each sentence.**

1. practices   practice

   Jake, Caleb, and Rhonda _____ their shooting every day.

   Sometimes Jake even _____ at night.

2. dribbles   dribble

   Caleb _____ the ball across the court.

   Then Jake and Rhonda _____ it.

3. shoots   shoot

   Rhonda _____ the ball, and she misses.

   Caleb and Jake _____ and miss.

4. jumps   jump

   The boys _____ for the rebound.

   Rhonda _____ , too.

2 Write your own sentences using the plural and singular verbs listed.

1. passes   pass

_____

_____

2. scores   score

_____

_____

3. cheers   cheer

_____

_____

4. joins   join

_____

_____

5. chooses   choose

_____

_____

Draw two lines under all of the singular verbs. What did you notice about all of them?

Using Irregular Verbs

1

Study the irregular verbs in the handbook. As a class, complete each set of sentences below with the correct forms of the irregular verb.

334

1. begin

   present: I _____ school at 8:30.

   past: Last year, school _____ at 8:00.

   past with *had*: When I got there, school had _____ at 8:30.

2. be

   present: I _____ in the third grade.

   past: Last year, I _____ in second grade.

   past with *had*: I had _____ looking forward to third grade.

3. catch

   present: I _____ a lot of balls at softball practice.

   past: In the last game, I _____ a fly ball.

   past with *had*: I had _____ two fly balls yesterday.

4. hide

   present: I _____ from my brother sometimes.

   past: Last night, I _____ in my closet.

   past with *have*: I have _____ there before.

Now complete the following set of sentences on your own. The directions are the same as in Part 1.

1. **fly**

   present: I _____ to Minneapolis every summer.

   past: Last year, I _____ by myself.

   past with *had*: I had _____ for years with my dad.

2. **come**

   present: Most days, I _____ to school with my sister.

   past: Yesterday, I _____ by myself.

   past with *have*: I have _____ by myself two times this month.

3. **throw**

   present: I _____ practice pitches every Friday.

   past: Last Friday, I _____ 30 pitches.

   past with *had*: I had _____ 25 pitches before I noticed how tired I was!

Write two sentences of your own using different forms of the verb *speak*.

1. _____

   _____

2. _____

   _____

Using Adjectives

335

* An **adjective** usually comes before the noun it describes.

Carrie planted <u>tiny</u> seeds.

What noun does the adjective
tiny describe in this sentence? _____

* Sometimes an adjective comes after a linking verb.

The seeds were <u>tiny</u>.

What noun does the adjective
tiny describe in this sentence? _____

1 **Underline the adjective in each sentence. Then draw an arrow to the noun it describes. (You're looking for the main describing word in each sentence, not _a, an,_ or _the._)**

Example: She used a <u>sharp</u> spade to dig.

1. Carrie planted red zinnias.

2. She watered the little seeds.

3. Green leaves soon popped up.

4. Bright sun shone on the plants.

5. Gentle rain watered them.

6. Fat buds formed.

7. Soon Carrie could pick a pretty bouquet of zinnias.

2 Draw a line under each adjective in the following sentences. Then draw an arrow to the noun it describes. All of the adjectives come after a linking verb.

Example: Grass is green.

1. Roses are red.
2. Violets are blue.
3. Sugar is sweet.
4. Words are true.

1. Daisies are white.
2. Marigolds are yellow.
3. Honey is sweet.
4. Sarah sure is mellow.

NEXT STOP   **Write a sentence for each of the adjective-noun pairs.**

Adjectives	Nouns
fluffy	➤ kitten
tough	➤ guy
beautiful	➤ song
silver	➤ earrings

1. _____

_____

2. _____

_____

3. _____

_____

4. _____

_____

Working with Adjectives

Adjectives have three different forms.

336

Positive: The pebble is <u>small</u>.

Comparative: The pebble is <u>smaller</u> than that rock.

Superlative: The pebble is the <u>smallest</u> stone in my collection.

1 Write sentences for the three forms of the adjectives listed below.

loud, louder, loudest

1. _____

_____

2. _____

_____

3. _____

_____

happy, happi...

1. _____

_____

2. _____

_____

3. _____

_____

2 Write a paragraph about one of the happiest times you have had in school.

_____

_____

_____

_____

_____

_____

_____

_____

_____

_____

_____

_____

_____

Circle the adjectives in your paragraph. How many times did you write an adjective in the comparative (ending in _er_) or the superlative form (ending in _est_)?

Adverbs

An **adverb** is a word that describes a verb, or tells how an action is done. Adverbs usually answer *when, where,* or *how.*

---

1 Adverbs of time tell *when or how often* an action is done. Fill in the blank in each sentence with one adverb from the list below.

yesterday	soon	now	first
tomorrow	later	weekly	last

1. Our class went to the toy museum _____.

2. I hope we can go back again _____.

3. In fact, I wish we could go _____.

---

2 Adverbs of place tell *where* something happens. Fill in the blank in each sentence with one adverb from the list below.

inside	here	up
outside	there	down

1. I told my mom I wanted to go _____ to play.

2. She looked _____ at me.

3. "Why don't you just play _____ ?" she asked.

3 Adverbs of manner tell *how* something is done. Fill in the blank in each sentence with one adverb from the list below.

quietly   carefully   slowly   happily
loudly   carelessly   quickly   sadly

1. I like to play my cassette player _____.

2. When I clean up my room, I do it very _____.

3. When it's time to eat, my cat comes running _____.

NEXT STOP Complete the list of "ly" words that is started here. Then in the space below write a brief story using at least three of your "ly" words.

1. _____softly_____   4. _____

2. _____lazily_____   5. _____

3. _____   6. _____

_____

_____

_____

_____

_____

_____

Name _____

Handbook Link

Using Prepositions

A phrase that begins with a preposition and ends with a noun is called a **prepositional phrase**.

Examples: to the lighthouse
in the boat
under the bridge
across the water
after breakfast

1 Draw a line under the prepositional phrase in each sentence below. Then circle each preposition.

Example: Mary was (in) deep water.

1. Mary was swimming against the tide.

2. She went backward with every stroke.

3. Waves washed over her head.

4. She was not near the beach.

5. Just then, she felt the nudge of a boat.

6. A lifeguard threw her a life preserver on a rope.

7. Mary reached for the rope.

8. The lifeguard rowed Mary toward the beach.

9. Mary said, "Thank you. I was really in danger."

Understanding Our Language **97**

Draw a line under the prepositional phrase in each sentence below. Then circle each preposition. (Some of these sentences have more than one prepositional phrase.)

Example: Pay attention (to) these rules (about) water safety.

1. Swim at beaches protected by lifeguards.

2. Never jump into strange waters.

3. Always look for underwater obstacles.

4. Do not swim in unmarked areas or in bad weather.

5. Always swim close to the shore and with a friend.

6. Go slowly into cold water.

7. Swim around other people.

8. Stay inside the buoys.

 **Create a sign for one of the safety rules above.**

Handbook Link

339

Conjunctions

A **conjunction** connects words or groups of words. The most common conjunctions are *and,* *but,* and *or.* There are three conjunctions in the following sentence:

Charley <u>and</u> Barbara wore their coats <u>and</u> hats, <u>but</u> forgot their boots.

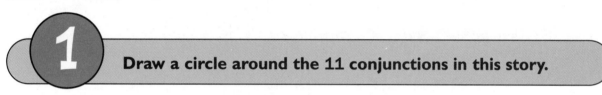

1 Draw a circle around the 11 conjunctions in this story.

The Sun and the Wind

Who is stronger, the sun or the wind? Well, once upon a time, they both thought they were stronger, and they began to argue.

"I am strong enough to make that man take off his hat, his scarf, and his coat," bragged the wind. The sun said nothing. It just hid behind a cloud.

The wind blew and blew, but the man did not take off his hat, his scarf, or his coat. Instead, he pulled them tighter and tighter to his body.

Then the sun came out, but it did so very quietly. Soon the man grew warm. He took off his hat, and he took off his scarf. Then he removed his coat.

Now do you know who is stronger? Is it the sun or the wind?

NEXT STOP

Write a sentence that answers the last two questions in the story.

_____

_____

Interjections

Hey! Let me tell you about interjections. An **interjection** is a word or phrase used to express strong emotion or surprise. It is followed by an exclamation point or a comma.

1 Draw a picture or design for each of the interjections. Write your own interjection in the last box, and draw a picture, too.

Hey! I did it!	Wow, I can't believe I just saw that!
Yuck! Look at all the bugs!	

2

Minilessons

The minilessons in this section cover basic editing and proofreading skills. You can work on the minilessons individually or in small groups.

Using Punctuation Minilessons

I love cookies. . . . . *Periods as End Punctuation*

WRITE a paragraph about your favorite food. Write at least four sentences. Leave out the periods at the end of your sentences. Then **TRADE** paragraphs with a partner. Put periods where they are needed in each other's paragraph.

First get a bowl. . . . . *Periods as End Punctuation*

Now **WRITE** a paragraph telling a friend how to prepare your favorite food. (If you're not sure how to make your favorite food, guess!) All your sentences should be requests. (See handbook page 296.)

Don't eat my shoes . . . please. . . . . *Periods as End Punctuation*

IMAGINE that you are taking care of a puppy. **WRITE** three request sentences that you might say to the puppy. Use periods correctly.

U. R. Terrific . . . . *Periods After Initials*

WRITE the first and middle initials plus the last name of each person in your family, your favorite movie or TV star, and your best friend. Be sure to use periods where they are needed.

Hungry Mungry Monkey .... *Periods After Initials*

PRETEND you are going to write a story about a family of monkeys. **MAKE UP** a last name for the family. Also make up first names and middle names for each of the monkeys. **WRITE OUT** the full names. Then **WRITE** the names using first and middle initials.

Mr. Hungry Mungry Monkey .... *Periods After Abbreviations*

MAKE UP an address for your monkey family. **ADDRESS** a letter to them. In your address, use at least three abbreviations. Use periods as needed.

> *EXAMPLE:* Mr. and Mrs. H. M. Monkey
> 123 Banana Ave.
> E. Monkey Town, Jungle Land 76543

Words into Numerals .... *Periods as Decimals*

WRITE the correct numerals for the words below. **PUT** decimal points where they are needed. The first two have been done for you.

1. One dollar and fifty cents $1.50
2. Ninety-eight point six   98.6
3. Five dollars and thirty-one cents   _____
4. Ten dollars   _____
5. Twenty dollars   _____
6. Two point four   _____
7. Sixteen point two   _____

A catfish is smooth, shiny, and slippery! .... Commas in a Series

WRITE a sentence using three words to describe an alligator. **PUT** commas where they are needed. Now **WRITE** sentences about two other animals. Use three describing words in each sentence. Don't forget the commas!

I like to cook, but . . . Commas in a Compound Sentence

WRITE a paragraph about something you like to do—drawing, singing, playing computer games, cooking, anything! Use all simple sentences. **TRADE** paragraphs with a partner. **COMBINE** some of your partner's simple sentences into compound sentences. (See handbook page 327.)

"The princess had warts," Carly said. .... Commas in Dialogue

IMAGINE that you and a friend are talking about a movie you've both seen. **WRITE DOWN** your conversation. **PUT** quotation marks and commas where they are needed. (See handbook pages 299 and 302.)

Commas, Commas, Commas .... Comma Review

OPEN your handbook to pages 297-299. Review all the ways commas are used. Now, on a separate sheet of paper, **WRITE** a sentence that uses commas to separate items in a series. Then **WRITE** a sentence that uses commas to set off a speaker's words. Finally, **WRITE** a sentence that uses a comma to make a compound sentence.

Count this way:
one, two, three ... . *Colon*

TURN to page 300 in your handbook. Read about using a colon to introduce a list. Then complete the following sentences. Use colons correctly. The first one has been done for you.

1. Here's one, two, three in Spanish : uno, dos, tres _____ .

2. These are my favorite animals _____ .

3. I collect these things _____ .

4. I don't like these foods _____ .

Don't forget contractions! .... *Contractions*

OPEN your handbook to page 301. Study the section on using apostrophes in contractions. Now **CLOSE** your handbook. **WRITE** the contractions of the following words. After you finish, go back to page 301 to check your work.

1. you are _____   4. they are _____

2. do not _____   5. is not _____

3. it is _____   6. was not _____

The raccoons' racket woke me up. . . . . *Possessives*

OPEN your handbook to page 301. Study the section on using apostrophes to show ownership. **WRITE** the possessive forms of the following nouns.

Singular Nouns	**Singular Possessive**
1. raccoon	_____
2. possum	_____
3. skunk	_____
4. squirrel	_____
5. gopher	_____

Plural Nouns	**Plural Possessive**
6. raccoons	_____
7. possums	_____
8. skunks	_____
9. squirrels	_____
10. gophers	_____

Are these one boy's toys or two boys' toys? .... Possessives

Each of the following sentences has a singular possessive. On a separate sheet of paper, **REWRITE** each sentence to make it a plural possessive. If you need help, turn to page 301 in your handbook. The first two sentences have been done for you.

1. The boy's markers are in the art closet.
    (Rewrite the sentence so that there is more than one boy.)
    The boys' markers are in the art closet.

2. The teacher's books are on the shelf.
    (Rewrite the sentence so that there is more than one teacher.)
    The teachers' books are on the shelf.

3. The girl's drawings are on the bulletin board.
    (Rewrite the sentence so that there is more than one girl.)

    _____

4. The cat's toys are all over the house.
    (Rewrite the sentence so that there is more than one cat.)

    _____

5. The neighbor's flowers are blooming.
    (Rewrite the sentence so that there is more than one neighbor.)

    _____

6. The dog's bones were buried in the backyard.
    (Rewrite the sentence so that there is more than one dog.)

    _____

The kids' lunches are smelly. .... *Plural Possessives*

REWRITE each sentence below. **TURN** the underlined subject into a possessive. The first one has been done for you.

1. The <u>students</u> have art supplies in the closet.

   > The students' art supplies are in the closet.

2. The <u>teachers</u> have computers in their offices.

3. The <u>children</u> have desks everywhere.

4. The <u>janitors</u> have keys that open everything!

The poem is called "True Blue." .... *Quotation Marks in Titles*

TURN to page 302 in your handbook. Review the section "To Punctuate Titles." Now **TURN** to the chapter "Writing Free-Verse Poetry," which begins on page 177. On the lines below, **WRITE** the names of the model poems in this chapter. Use quotation marks correctly.

1. _____

2. _____

3. _____

"Hi. I'm Seth," I said. . . . . *Quotation Marks*

IMAGINE that there is a new kid in your class. You are talking to her for the very first time. **WRITE** a dialogue that tells what you might say to each other. Be sure to use quotation marks correctly.

Where do you draw the line? . . . . *Hyphens*

OPEN your handbook to page 303. **READ** about using a hyphen to divide a word. Then look again at the sample paragraph about hawks. Can you find other words, besides *grasshopper,* that you can divide with a hyphen? (Remember, a word must have at least two syllables to be divided with a hyphen.) **WRITE DOWN** two of the words you think could be divided. Then look them up in a dictionary. The dictionary will show you where to put the hyphen.

Look out! What for? . . . . *End Punctuation*

BEGIN a dialogue with a partner. One person makes exclamations. The other person asks questions.

> EXAMPLE: "Look out!"
> "What for?"
> "The bear!"
> "Where?"
> "Behind you!"
> "What should I do?"
> "Run!"

Make sure you use quotation marks before and after the spoken words. (See page 302 in your handbook for help.) Finally, you and your partner may **READ** the story for the whole class.

Q and A . . . . End Punctuation

WORK with a partner. **WRITE** a sentence that is a question. Have
your partner write an answer that ends with an exclamation point.
Then have your partner write a question, and you write an answer.

QUESTION: What do you do if you see a turtle sleeping
in the road?

ANSWER: Grab it!

He (our neighbor) is nice. . . . . Parentheses

TURN to page 304 in your handbook. Review "Parentheses." In
each of the following sentences, **ADD** the words you see after the
sentence. Put the words in parentheses. A star shows where to put
them. The first one has been done for you.

1. Our neighbor ★ grows roses.   **the one next door**

   Our neighbor (the one next door) grows roses.
   _____

2. He gave me one in my favorite color ★.   **pink**

   _____

3. I put it in a vase ★.   **a jar, really**

   _____

4. The next day ★ he gave me another rose.   **Sunday**

   _____

5. A loud crash ★ woke me in the night.   **thunder, I think**

   _____

Checking Mechanics Minilessons

The Name Game .... *Capitalization*

OPEN your handbook to page 309, "Capitalizing Geographic Names." For each type of name listed (Planets and heavenly bodies, Continents, and so on), **LIST** another example. Do as many as you can on your own. **CHECK** a map or an atlas if you need help.

And on this farm there were some . . . . *Plurals*

WRITE a paragraph about animals on a farm. **USE** the plural forms of the following words. If you get stuck, turn to page 310 in your handbook for help.

donkey

bunny

fox

cow

horse

goose

Words or numerals? .... *Numbers*

STUDY page 311 in your handbook. Then **FILL IN** the blanks in the following sentences. **WRITE** either "words" or "numerals," whichever is correct. Look back at page 311 to check your work.

1. When numbers begin a sentence, they are always written as _____.

2. Numbers less than 10 are almost always written as _____.

3. Numbers greater than 10 are almost always written as _____.

4. When you write very large numbers, you can use a combination of

   _____ and _____.

5. Numbers that are in dates, times, and addresses are written as _____.

6. Numbers that are amounts of money are written as _____.

Mail from AL to WY .... *Abbreviations*

OPEN your handbook to page 313. On the chart of state abbreviations, **LOOK UP** the postal abbreviations for the following places. The first one has been done for you.

Texas ___TX___   District of Columbia _____

New York _____   Michigan _____

Florida _____   California _____

Utah _____   West Virginia _____

Kansas _____   Connecticut _____

Indiana _____   Mississippi _____

What does that spell? .... *Acronyms*

TURN to page 312 in your handbook. Study the section "Acronyms." Then **WRITE** the acronyms for the following phrases.

Rainforest Action Network _____

Performing Animal Welfare Society _____

Handicapped Equestrian Learning Program _____

North Atlantic Treaty Organization _____

Cooperative (for) American Relief Everywhere _____

Mothers Against Drunk Driving _____

National Aeronautics (and) Space Administration _____

Understanding Sentences Minilessons

What do you know? . . . . *Sentence Fragments*

WRITE sentence fragments that give facts about people in your class. Write two fragments that need a verb. (*EXAMPLE:* Last summer, Kirsten.) Write two fragments that need a subject. (*EXAMPLE:* Has a pet snake.) **TRADE** with a partner. Try to turn each other's fragments into correct, complete sentences.

Not a Sentence . . . . *Sentence Fragments*

Below are some sentence fragments that need both a subject and a predicate. On a separate sheet of paper, **MAKE** each fragment into a correct sentence. The first one has been done for you.

After the rain.

      EXAMPLE: We charged outside after the rain.

At the mall.   Before lunch.   In the backyard.

Fixing Fragments . . . . *Sentence Fragments*

CHOOSE a paragraph from one of your favorite books or stories. **TURN** three or four sentences in the paragraph into sentence fragments. (See page 71 in your handbook.) Take the subjects out of some sentences. Take the predicates out of others. **TRADE** with a partner. **CORRECT** each other's fragments by making them into complete sentences. Finally, **COMPARE** your sentences with those in the book or story. (They don't have to be the same; they just have to be correct.)

Put a stop to run-ons! .... *Run-On Sentences*

CHOOSE a paragraph from one of your favorite books or stories. **TURN** some of the sentences into run-on sentences. (See page 71 in your handbook for an explanation.) **TRADE** with a partner. **CORRECT** each other's run-ons by turning each one into two correct sentences. Finally, **COMPARE** your corrected sentences with the sentences in the book or story. (They don't have to be the same, but they do have to be correct.)

It goes on and on and on . . . . *Run-On Sentences*

LIST two things that you think go on for too long. (Winter? Your mom's business trip?) Then **WRITE** two run-on sentences about these things.

> EXAMPLE: I went to my sister's dance practice I thought it would never end.

TRADE papers with a partner. **CORRECT** the run-on sentences in each other's work by adding commas and connecting words.

My Favorite Movie .... *Sentence Errors*

TURN the following sentence fragment into a complete sentence:

My favorite movie.

> EXAMPLE: My favorite movie is Pocahontas.

Now **TURN** your complete sentence into a run-on sentence by adding another complete thought to it.

> EXAMPLE: My favorite movie is Pocahontas I really like the music.

Finally, **CORRECT** your run-on sentence.

> EXAMPLE: My favorite movie is Pocahontas. I really like the music.

Lizzie the Lizard .... Sentence Combining

COMBINE each pair of sentences below into one sentence. First
   CIRCLE the key word or words in the second sentence. Then
   WRITE a new sentence by moving the key word or phrase from the
   second sentence into the first sentence.

EXAMPLE: Emily has a pet. It is a ⟨lizard.⟩
                     Emily has a pet lizard.

1. Lizzie the lizard likes people. She likes them a lot.

2. Emily takes Lizzie out on a leash. The leash is green.

3. Lizzie sits and watches people. She sits on Emily's shoulder.

Cold, Creamy, and Sweet .... Sentence Combining

WRITE three sentences describing your favorite food. Then try to
   COMBINE all three sentences into one sentence. Look at page 73 in
   your handbook for different ways to combine sentences.

Putting It All Together .... Sentence Combining

GET OUT a piece of your own writing: a paragraph, a story, or a
   report. **READ** your writing, looking for sentences you can combine.
   When you find two sentences to combine, **WRITE** your new
   sentence on a separate sheet of paper. Try to write at least two
   new sentences.

What is where? . . . . *Sentence Combining*

FILL IN the blanks in the sentences below. Use the map on page 354 of your handbook to help you. Then **COMBINE** each set of sentences into one sentence. (See page 73 in your handbook, "Combine with Compound Subjects.") The first one has been done for you.

Mississippi is near Florida.
Alabama is near Florida.

1. ___Georgia_____ is near Florida.

2. __Mississippi, Alabama, and Georgia are near Florida._____

Arizona is just north of Mexico.
New Mexico is just north of Mexico.

3. _____ is just north of Mexico.

4. _____

Montana is on Canada's border.
North Dakota on Canada's border.

5. _____ is on Canada's border.

6. _____

Washington is on the Pacific Ocean.
Oregon is on the Pacific Ocean.

7. _____ is on the Pacific Ocean.

8. _____

We went swimming and ate nachos. .... *Compound Subjects and Predicates*

IMAGINE that you could have any kind of birthday party you wanted. **WRITE** a paragraph about your party. Write at least two sentences with compound subjects, and two sentences with compound verbs. (See pages 325-326 in your handbook to review compound subjects and compound verbs.)

EXAMPLES: Moe and Dave came to my party. (compound subject)

We ate cake and rode on a roller coaster. (compound verb)

Which is it? .... *Simple and Compound Sentences*

GET OUT an old story or report you have written. **PICK OUT** all of the simple and compound sentences. (See page 327 in your handbook to review simple and compound sentences.) **WRITE** an S at the beginning of each simple sentence. **WRITE** a C at the beginning of each compound sentence.

Making Compound Sentences .... *Simple and Compound Sentences*

USE the same story or report that you used in the last minilesson. **LOOK** for places where there are two simple sentences next to each other. **REWRITE** them as one compound sentence.

Be a sentence detective. .... *Kinds of Sentences*

TURN to page 251 in your handbook. **READ** the student model "Skunks." **FIND** one example of each kind of sentence— declarative, interrogative, imperative, and exclamatory—in this writing. (Page 327 in your handbook explains the different kinds of sentences.) This is a good activity to do with a partner.

"You went where?" .... *Kinds of Sentences*

TURN to page 168 in your handbook. **READ** the student model "The Dinosaur Club." Now **IMAGINE** that when Maya gets home, her dad asks her where she has been. **WRITE** a dialogue about what Maya and her dad say to each other. Make sure you use all four kinds of sentences listed on page 327 of your handbook. Here is one way Maya's talk with her dad could start:
> "Maya, where were you? Supper's almost ready."
> "Dad, you'll never guess!"

Finding Subjects and Predicates .... *Parts of a Sentence*

CHOOSE an old story or report you have written. In each of your sentences, draw one line under the simple subject and two lines under the simple predicate. (See handbook pages 325-326.) Things to remember:

1. Compound sentences will have two subjects and two predicates.
2. Some simple sentences may have a compound subject or a compound verb.

What's the subject? . . . . Sentences: Subjects

WRITE these three words at the top of a piece of paper: *people, places,* and *things*. **LIST** three nouns under each of these words. Now **WRITE** three sentences, using nouns in your list as the simple subjects in your sentences. **UNDERLINE** the complete subject in each sentence. (See handbook page 325.)

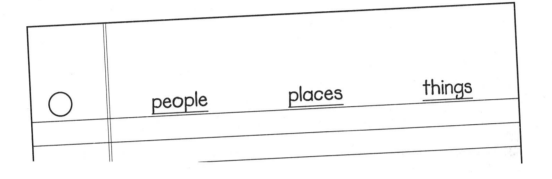

What's the predicate? . . . . Sentences: Predicates

LIST five of your favorite action words. (You may like *giggle* or *dribble*.) **WRITE** three sentences, using action words in your list as the simple predicates in your sentences. **UNDERLINE** the complete predicate in each sentence. (See handbook page 326.)

Building Sentences . . . . . . Sentences: Subjects and Predicates

On a separate sheet of paper, **WRITE** a simple subject, a compound subject, a simple predicate, and a compound predicate. (Check pages 325 and 326 in your handbook to review subjects and predicates.) Now **TRADE** papers with your partner. **WRITE** four complete sentences using the subjects and predicates your partner wrote.

At the top of a sheet of paper, **WRITE** the following sentence:
I love bugs. **REWRITE** the sentence using a different subject.
Then have a partner **REWRITE** the sentence using a different
subject. Now you **REWRITE** the sentence again—this time using a
different predicate. Keep trading back and forth with your partner.
Rewrite the sentence with many different subjects and predicates.

> *EXAMPLE:*
>
> I love bugs.
>
> Casey loves bugs.   (different subject)
>
> Sacha loves bugs.   (different subject)
>
> Sacha chases bugs.   (different predicate)

ADD different describing words to make your sentences fun.

> Silly Sacha eats bugs.   (describing word plus different predicate)
>
> Dawn eats ugly, fuzzy bugs.   (different subject plus two describing words)

Understanding Our Language Minilessons

Calling All Nouns . . . . *Nouns*

PRACTICE finding nouns. (Remember, a noun names a person, a place, a thing, or an idea.) First **TURN** to page 88 in your handbook. **FIND** all the nouns in the paragraph "Short and Quick." **LIST** the nouns below. (*Hint: Someone* is a pronoun, not a noun. There are eight nouns in all.)

1. _____   5. _____

2. _____   6. _____

3. _____   7. _____

4. _____   8. _____

Name One . . . . *Common and Proper Nouns*

TURN to page 329 in your handbook. Review "Common Nouns and Proper Nouns." Next to each common noun below, **WRITE** a proper noun that matches it. If you have trouble thinking of a proper noun, use the maps in your handbook to help you. They are on pages 353-362. The first two examples have been done for you.

1. planet ___Earth___   5. river _____

2. country ___Mexico___   6. mountains _____

3. state _____   7. ocean _____

4. city _____   8. lake _____

Columbus sailed the ocean blue. . . . . *Common and Proper Nouns*

OPEN your handbook to page 382. **LOOK** at the top part of the page, "U.S. History." On a separate sheet of paper, **MAKE** two lists of nouns. First **LIST** three common nouns you find in this section. Then **LIST** five proper nouns. (*Hint:* Not every word that begins with a capital letter is a proper noun. Some capitalized words may be describing words.)

One or more than one? . . . . . . *Singular and Plural Nouns*

TURN to page 382 in your handbook. **LOOK** at the section "Science & Inventions." On a separate sheet of paper, make two lists of nouns. First **LIST** all the plural nouns in this section. Then **LIST** all the singular nouns. There are five plural nouns and three singular nouns. One of the singular nouns is proper.

Plural Nouns

1. _____

2. _____

3. _____

4. _____

5. _____

Singular Nouns

1. _____

2. _____

3. _____

Whose hair? . . . . *Possessive Pronouns*

TURN to page 330 in your handbook. **READ** about "Possessive Pronouns." Then **USE** each of the following possessive pronouns in a sentence. Make all your sentences about hair. The first one has been done for you.

1. **their:** Tracey and Maria wear their hair the same way.

2. **your:** _____

3. **my:** _____

4. **our:** _____

What a joke! . . . . *Personal Pronouns*

TURN to page 330 in your handbook. **READ** about "Common Personal Pronouns." Now turn to page 90. Read the friendly note under "To Share Something You Know." **LIST** all the personal pronouns you find in this note. There are six of them.

We flew in a helicopter. . . . . *Types of Verbs*

OPEN your handbook to page 331. **REVIEW** "Types of Verbs." Now **WRITE** three sentences about something your whole class did together. It could be a project or a field trip. In your first sentence, use an action verb. In your second sentence, use a linking verb. In your third sentence, use a helping verb.

Action, Linking, Helping . . . . *Types of Verbs*

WRITE at least four or five sentences about something you did during the past weekend. (The more you write, the better.) Then **REVIEW** "Types of Verbs" on page 331. **DRAW** two lines under at least three of the verbs in your writing. **LABEL** these verbs as either action (A), linking (L), or helping (H).

Play / Played / Will Play . . . . *Tense of Verbs*

REVIEW "Tense of Verbs" on page 332 in your handbook. **WRITE** a sentence in the present tense. Make your sentence about a game or sport you like to play. Now **REWRITE** your sentence using the past tense. Finally, write your sentence again, but this time use the future tense.

It will snow tomorrow. . . . . *Tense of Verbs*

TURN to page 56 in your handbook. Read the model "Snow Day!" All the verbs in this paragraph are in the past tense. Now **PRETEND** that you can predict the future. As you read the model aloud, **CHANGE** all the verbs to future tense. (*Hint:* You'll use the word *will* in every sentence.) We've written the first sentence below to get you started.

It will snow a lot tomorrow, so school will let out early.

Verbs and Donuts .... *Singular and Plural Verbs*

In each sentence below, **FILL IN** the correct form of the verb shown at the beginning of the sentence. The first one has been done for you.

make 1. Kayla's mom ____makes____ donuts.

   My parents ____make____ donuts.

put 2. She _____ sprinkles on top.

   They _____ sprinkles on top.

bring 3. Kayla _____ one for lunch every day.

   We _____ one for lunch every day.

have 4. Kayla _____ a donut.

   We _____ a donut.

do 5. Watch what she _____ with it.

   Watch what we _____ with it.

give 6. Kayla _____ one donut to a friend.

   We _____ one donut to a friend.

say 7. Kayla _____ thanks for the donuts.

   We _____ thanks for the donuts.

love 8. She _____ eating decorated donuts.

   We _____ eating decorated donuts.

Two Little Brothers . . . . *Subject-Verb Agreement*

REVIEW "Singular and Plural Verbs" on page 333 in your handbook. Now **TURN** to page 60. Look at the model "Living with a Little Brother." **IMAGINE** that the writer has two little brothers instead of one. **READ** the model aloud. Every time you see the word *he,* change it to *they.* You'll also need to change all the verbs to plural verbs. We've written the first three sentences to get you started.

Living with my little brothers can be hard. First, they try to copy me. If I have a second glass of milk, they do, too.

_____

_____

_____

_____

_____

_____

_____

_____

_____

He eats grapes.
We eat grapes. . . . . *Subject-Verb Agreement*

TURN to page 333 in your handbook. **REVIEW** "Singular and Plural Verbs." Now **WRITE** two sentences about grapes. Your first sentence should have a singular subject and a singular verb. Your second sentence should have a plural subject and a plural verb. You can use the sentences in your handbook to give you ideas.

Is it "singed" or "sang"? . . . . *Irregular Verbs*

OPEN your handbook to page 334. Look over the chart of irregular verbs. **PICK** two verbs that you have a hard time remembering. **USE** the past tense of each verb you picked in a sentence.

Describe It . . . . *Adjectives*

REVIEW "Adjectives" on page 335 in your handbook. Now turn to page 185. Read the haiku at the bottom of the page. It begins "See the red berries . . ." **FIND** the three adjectives in the haiku. Then **REPLACE** all three adjectives with new ones. Use any adjectives you want! See how your adjectives change the whole poem?

Quickly or slowly? . . . . *Adverbs*

TURN to page 337 in your handbook. **REVIEW** "Adverbs." On a separate sheet of paper, **DRAW** a describing wheel. (If you need to see what a describing wheel looks like, turn to page 265.) The subject of your describing wheel is *run*. **ADD** as many adverbs as you can think of. *Remember:* Adverbs can tell *how* something is done, *where* it is done, or *when* it is done.

Prepositions in a Poem . . . . *Prepositions*

TURN to page 338 in your handbook. **READ** about "Prepositions." Now **TURN** to page 180. Look at the poem "When I Grow Up." **FIND** the prepositional phrases in this poem. (There are five of them.) **WRITE** the phrases on your own paper and **CIRCLE** the preposition in each one.

Zoom! My bike flew down the hill. . . . . *Interjections*

OPEN your handbook to page 339. **READ** about "Interjections." Now **WRITE** two sentences of your own that use interjections. Don't use the same interjections that your handbook uses. Come up with two of your own!

MUG Shot Sentences

These activities review basic writing skills—mechanics, usage, and grammar. This daily practice helps you with your proofreading skills.

Focused SENTENCES

* **End Punctuation**

    Michael's family went out west last summer

* **End Punctuation**

    Did you hear about his adventure

* **End Punctuation**

    Michael and his sister Katie got lost in the canyon

* **End Punctuation**

    Katie stepped on a rattlesnake

* **End Punctuation**

    Their parents were so glad to find them before dark

Focused SENTENCES

* **Periods (In Initials and Abbreviations)**

    Michael J Fox is an actor.

* **Periods (In Initials and Abbreviations)**

    Dr Johnson's office is on N Main St.

* **Periods (In Initials and Abbreviations)**

    A A Milne is one of Ms Anderson's favorite authors.

* **Periods (In Initials and Abbreviations)**

    Dan M Langford, Jr , is the son of Dan M Langford, Sr.

* **Periods (In Initials and Abbreviations)**

    Mrs Rose's bakery is on E Spice Ave.

Focused SENTENCES

✶ **Commas (In a Series)**

Cheese yogurt and milk are all dairy products.

✶ **Commas (In a Series)**

Susan likes to read books write letters and play the piano.

✶ **Commas (In a Series)**

Josh has been to Michigan Wisconsin Ohio and Pennsylvania.

✶ **Commas (In a Series)**

Matthew will invite Robin Joe Steve and Zach to his party.

✶ **Commas (In a Series)**

Dad washes the car mows the lawn and plays with us.

Focused SENTENCES

* **Commas (To Keep Numbers Clear)**

   Troop 4 8 0 sold 1 5 3 4 boxes of Girl Scout cookies this year.

* **Commas (To Keep Numbers Clear)**

   There are about 4 3 0 0 0 people in our community.

* **Commas (To Keep Numbers Clear)**

   Harry's antique car is worth between $3 0 0 0 0 and $4 0 0 0 0!

* **Commas (To Keep Numbers Clear)**

   We have over 3 5 0 0 books in our school library. The city library has more than 1 0 0 0 0 books.

* **Commas (To Keep Numbers Clear)**

   Michigan Stadium can seat more than 1 0 6 0 0 0 fans for a football game!

Focused SENTENCES

* **Commas**
  (In City and State; Between Day and Year in a Date)

  Darrin wrote a letter to his Uncle Frank in Durham North Carolina.

* **Commas (In City and State; Between Day and Year in a Date)**

  He mailed the letter on June 14 1995.

* **Commas (In City and State; Between Day and Year in a Date)**

  Darrin now lives in Birmingham Michigan.

* **Commas (In City and State; Between Day and Year in a Date)**

  The letter was stamped at the post office in Royal Oak Michigan.

* **Commas (In City and State; Between Day and Year in a Date)**

  Uncle Frank received Darrin's letter on June 18 1995.

Focused SENTENCES

* **Commas (In a Compound Sentence)**

   I ate all my potatoes and I even tried some spinach.

* **Commas (In a Compound Sentence)**

   My sister hid her lima beans and our dog ate every one!

* **Commas (In a Compound Sentence)**

   My dad took us to see a movie but he didn't buy us any popcorn.

* **Commas (In a Compound Sentence)**

   Joey invited me to his house but I had too much homework to do.

* **Commas (In a Compound Sentence)**

   We could play basketball after school or we could go in-line skating.

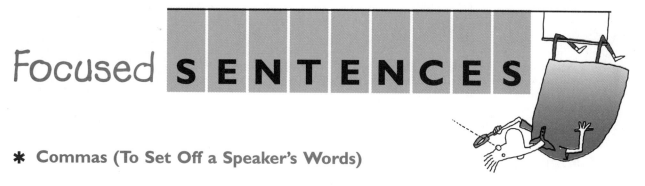

Focused SENTENCES

* **Commas (To Set Off a Speaker's Words)**

  Dad said " Who wants to go for a bike ride? "

* **Commas (To Set Off a Speaker's Words)**

  I yelled " I do, I do! "

* **Commas (To Set Off a Speaker's Words)**

  " Don't forget to wear your helmet " Mom called.

* **Commas (To Set Off a Speaker's Words)**

  I asked Dad " Can Matthew come, too? "

* **Commas (To Set Off a Speaker's Words)**

  " Yes " Dad answered. " Why don't you call him right now? "

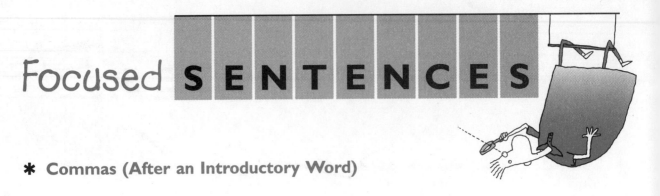

Focused SENTENCES

✱ **Commas (After an Introductory Word)**

Karen can you help me untie this knot?

✱ **Commas (After an Introductory Word)**

Goodness that was a loud bang!

✱ **Commas (After an Introductory Word)**

Jennifer will you please share your sandwich with me?

✱ **Commas (After an Introductory Word)**

Grandma you make the best apple pies!

✱ **Commas (After an Introductory Word)**

Hey I can do that trick, too!

Focused SENTENCES

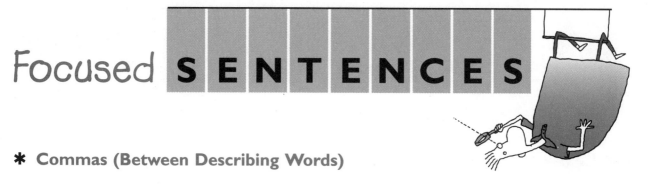

* **Commas (Between Describing Words)**

    Rachel's poodle has short curly hair.

* **Commas (Between Describing Words)**

    John's cat has long silky fur.

* **Commas (Between Describing Words)**

    I love the sweet tart taste of caramel apples.

* **Commas (Between Describing Words)**

    Joe and Bryce gobbled up the hot spicy pizza.

* **Commas (Between Describing Words)**

    We live on a wide shady street.

Focused SENTENCES

* **Colons**

   We eat lunch at 11 30 a.m.

* **Colons**

   " Dear Mr. Mayer " is the salutation in Karen's business
   letter.

* **Colons**

   I had to do three chores on Saturday walk the dog,
   unload the dishwasher, and help with the laundry.

* **Colons**

   Our baseball games always start at 7 30.

* **Colons**

   My brother has three friends Benjamin, David, and
   Logan.

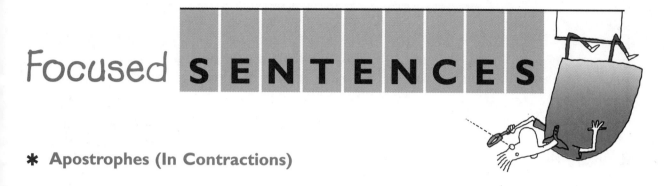

Focused SENTENCES

* **Apostrophes (In Contractions)**

  Its time for recess.

* **Apostrophes (In Contractions)**

  I think youre a great friend!

* **Apostrophes (In Contractions)**

  Alaska wasnt the fiftieth state to join the union.

* **Apostrophes (In Contractions)**

  I dont like doing chores, but I always get them done.

* **Apostrophes (In Contractions)**

  The boys think theyre going to win the race.

Focused SENTENCES

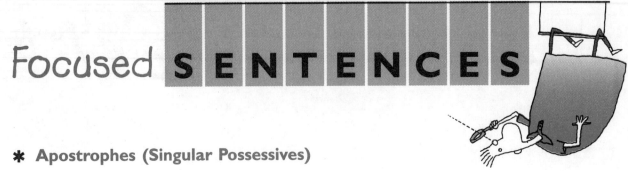

✳ **Apostrophes (Singular Possessives)**

   Kyles bicycle is blue and red.

✳ **Apostrophes (Singular Possessives)**

   Yesterday I rode in Joeys go-cart.

✳ **Apostrophes (Singular Possessives)**

   Nicole had to use Matthews spelling book to study
   her words.

✳ **Apostrophes (Singular Possessives)**

   Our neighbors garden is full of tomatoes!

✳ **Apostrophes (Singular Possessives)**

   My teachers first name is a secret.

Focused **SENTENCES**

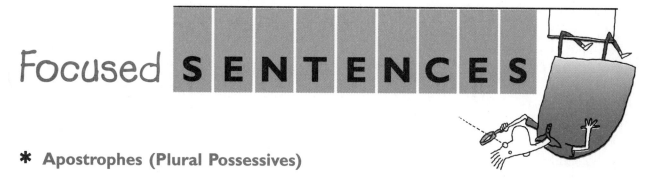

* **Apostrophes (Plural Possessives)**

    The boys team finished second in the three-legged race.

* **Apostrophes (Plural Possessives)**

    The childrens choir sang in the concert.

* **Apostrophes (Plural Possessives)**

    My friends names are JoAnn and Nancy.

* **Apostrophes (Plural Possessives)**

    The womens locker room is down the hall.

* **Apostrophes (Plural Possessives)**

    I saw two swans nests at our lake.

Focused SENTENCES

✱ **Quotation Marks (In Dialogue)**

Let's go to the beach today, Mom said.

✱ **Quotation Marks (In Dialogue)**

Hooray, my sister and brother yelled.

✱ **Quotation Marks (In Dialogue)**

Mom said, We need to clear away the breakfast dishes.

✱ **Quotation Marks (In Dialogue)**

I'll get the dishcloth to wipe the table, I called.

✱ **Quotation Marks (In Dialogue)**

Great, Mom said. Now I'll pack our beach bag, and then we can go!

Focused SENTENCES

* **Quotation Marks (Titles)**

   The Homework Machine is one of my favorite poems.

* **Underlining (Titles)**

   Pocahontas and The Lion King are recent Disney movies.

* **Quotation Marks (Titles)**

   We all sang The Star-Spangled Banner before the
   game began.

* **Underlining (Titles)**

   National Geographic World is an awesome magazine
   for kids.

* **Underlining (Titles)**

   Beverly Cleary wrote Ramona the Pest and many other
   children's books.

Planets

✳ **Commas (In a Series), Capitalization**

Mercury venus earth and mars are all planets.

✳ **Commas (In a Compound Sentence), Capitalization**

A year on Earth is 365 days long but a year on mercury is only 88 days long.

✳ **Apostrophes (In Contractions), Using the Right Word**

I wouldnt go to Pluto because its two cold and too far away.

✳ **Capitalization, Forms of Verbs, End Punctuation**

Did you know that saturn and uranus both has rings

✳ **Forms of Adjectives, Apostrophes (To Show Ownership)**

Our atmosphere is more better than Jupiters atmosphere.

Using Maps

* **Apostrophes (In Contractions), Using the Right Word, Capitalization**

    Youll want to pack warm close if you go to alaska in the winter.

* **Capitalization, Colons, Commas (In a Series)**

    Three oceans surround north america the arctic the pacific and the atlantic.

* **Using the Right Word, Capitalization, Run-On Sentence**

    My family drove threw six states to get to florida that was the greatest vacation I ever had.

* **Capitalization, Run-On Sentence, Apostrophes (In Contractions)**

    The largest American desert is the mojave its in the state of california.

* **Quotation Marks, Commas (To Set Off a Speaker's Words), Commas (Between Describing Words)**

    Lake Superior is a cold beautiful lake said the park ranger.

Using Maps

* **Commas (In City and State), Commas (In a Compound Sentence)**

   Mark received a postcard from Orlando Florida and it was a picture of Mickey Mouse.

* **Forms of Verbs, Commas (In a Compound Sentence), Capitalization**

   We was in Utah on our vacation and we floated in the great salt lake.

* **Capitalization, Run-On Sentence, Commas (To Keep Numbers Clear)**

   Rhode island is the smallest state it has only 1 2 1 4 square miles.

* **Punctuation (After an Introductory Word), Commas (To Keep Numbers Clear)**

   Wow Alaska has a mountain that is 2 0 3 2 0 feet high.

* **Forms of Verbs, Capitalization, Commas (To Keep Numbers Clear), End Punctuation**

   Did you knew that the mississippi river is 2 3 4 0 miles long

Proofreading SENTENCES

U.S. History

* **Capitalization, Commas (Between Day and Year in a Date)**

   The Declaration of independence was signed on July 4 1776.

* **Capitalization, Commas (In a Compound Sentence), Numbers**

   The civil war started in 1861 and it ended 5 years later in 1865.

* **Using the Right Word, Capitalization**

   Pioneers crossed many rivers and creaks as they traveled to oregon and california.

* **Tenses of Verbs, Capitalization, Commas (Between Day and Year in a Date)**

   The United States enter world war II on December 7 1941.

* **Using the Right Word, Commas (In a Compound Sentence)**

   It is now common to sea airplanes in the sky but in 1903 airplanes were brand-new.

U.S. History

✳ Colons, Commas (In a Series)

Here are some inventions that changed our world telephones airplanes and rockets.

✳ Periods (In Initials), Capitalization, Run-On Sentence

Martin Luther King, jr , fought for civil rights he believed everyone should be treated fairly.

✳ Forms of Verbs, Capitalization

Charles Lindbergh became a hero when he flown across the atlantic ocean in 1927.

✳ Using the Right Word, Periods (In Abbreviations), End Punctuation

Did you no there is a U S flag on the moon

✳ Capitalization, Numbers, End Punctuation

Are Alaska and hawaii our 2 newest states

Using Reference Materials

* **Quotation Marks, Commas (In a Series), Periods (In Abbreviations)**

  Encyclopedias dictionaries and atlases are all reference books, said Ms Waters.

* **Plurals, Capitalization, Commas (In a Compound Sentence)**

  Jon looked for two biographys of thomas edison but he found only one.

* **Commas (To Set Off a Speaker's Words), Quotation Marks, Titles**

  Mrs. Cooper said Look in a book called From Sea to Shining Sea for facts about the states.

* **Capitalization, Titles**

  If you have to do a report on france or spain, look for information in the World Almanac or in an encyclopedia.

* **Apostrophes (To Show Ownership), Forms of Verbs**

  Hillarys favorite part of the library are the nonfiction section.

Using Reference Materials

* **Capitalization, Commas (In a Series), End Punctuation**

  the table of contents the glossary and the index help you find information in books

* **Periods (In Abbreviations), Titles, Capitalization**

  Dr Seuss is the author of Green eggs and Ham.

* **Using the Right Word, Commas (In a Compound Sentence)**

  I waited four my turn on the computer but the bell rang before I could use it.

* **Forms of Verbs, Run-On Sentence**

  Benji take a map of the library along it included many interesting details.

* **Quotation Marks, Punctuation (After an Introductory Word), Commas (Between Day and Year in a Date)**

  Bruce shouted, Wow I found a book that was first checked out on March 15 1947!

Proofreading SENTENCES

A History of the Language

* **Using the Right Word, Capitalization, End Punctuation**

    Do you know wear the english language came from

* **Capitalization, Commas (In a Series)**

    There are french german and spanish words in our language.

* **Capitalization, Run-On Sentence**

    Some english words become part of other languages the word "weekend" means the same in french and english.

* **Commas (In a Series), Capitalization, End Punctuation**

    We learned animal names such as moose opossum and chipmunk from the native Americans

* **Using the Right Word, Commas (In a Compound Sentence), Capitalization**

    I never new that "alphabet" was a greek word but I do know that "pizza" is italian!

A History of the Language

✳ **Capitalization, Using the Right Word**

the first printed books were maid in london in the 1400's.

✳ **Capitalization, Using the Right Word, Sentence Fragments**

The spanish added some of there words to the english language. Cigar, canyon, and rodeo.

✳ **Forms of Verbs, Capitalization, Titles**

We sing the french song Frère Jacques in music last year.

✳ **Apostrophes (In Contractions), Run-On Sentence**

Its interesting to watch deaf people talk their hands move so quickly!

✳ **Capitalization, Commas (In a Compound Sentence)**

Louis braille became blind as a child and he invented the Braille alphabet.

A History of the Language

* **Using the Right Word, Commas (To Keep Numbers Clear), Capitalization**

   Their are more than 5 0 0 0 0 0 words in the english language.

* **Capitalization, Titles**

   The little Prince is a famous french book.

* **Apostrophes (In Contractions), Capitalization**

   Its hard for students from other countries to learn english as a second language.

* **Commas (In a Series), Run-On Sentence**

   Words like *through though* and *tough* are hard to learn they look like they should rhyme.

* **Capitalization, Sentence Fragments**

   You feel the braille alphabet with your fingers. Need special tools to write in braille.

Proofreading SENTENCES

Greetings

✱ **Quotation Marks, Commas (To Set Off a Speaker's Words)**

Bonjour said the French visitor.

✱ **Quotation Marks, Commas (To Set Off a Speaker's Words)**

Adios called Juan as he walked away.

✱ **Using the Right Word, Capitalization**

I think ant carla speaks italian very well.

✱ **Capitalization, Titles**

Children can learn spanish and english words while watching sesame street.

✱ **Using the Right Word, Capitalization**

Joe knows how to right sentences in english and italian.

Measurement

* **Using the Right Word, Capitalization**

  Sixteen ounces equal won pound in the united states system of measurement.

* **Commas (In a Series), End Punctuation**

  The metric system is used in medicine science and some other areas

* **Using the Right Word, Numbers**

  A paper clip ways about 1 gram.

* **Quotation Marks, Hyphens (In Fractions)**

  There are about two and one half centimeters in one inch, said Mr. Anderson.

* **Apostrophes (In Contractions), Sentence Fragments**

  If you dont have a ruler, use a quarter to measure something small. About one inch wide.

Graphics

* **Commas (In a Series), Commas (In a Compound Sentence)**

  Tables symbols and diagrams are kinds of graphics and they can help you learn.

* **Using the Right Word, Sentence Fragments**

  The heart symbol stands four a feeling. Means love.

* **Using the Right Word, Commas (In a Series)**

  Blue rode signs usually mean that food gas or medical care is near.

* **Forms of Verbs, Plurals**

  We draw diagrams of butterflys and frogs last year.

* **Using the Right Word, Commas (In a Compound Sentence)**

  Jim and Eric labeled there diagram and they colored it with bright colors.

Graphics

* **Numbers, Run-On Sentence**

   Alyssa took a survey of thirty-five students then she made a table to organize the information.

* **Rambling Sentence, Apostrophes (In Contractions)**

   Five kids have fish and four kids have hamsters and eight kids have dogs and three kids dont have any pets.

* **Forms of Verbs, Sentence Fragments**

   A table are an easy way to find facts. Has rows and columns.

* **Quotation Marks, Commas (After an Introductory Word)**

   Mark please tell us what's for lunch today, said Ms. Romano.

* **Capitalization, Commas (In a Series), End Punctuation**

   tables can use words numbers and symbols to tell information

Graphics

* **Titles, Commas (In a Series)**

    TV Guide gives a table of times channels and programs for each night.

* **Titles, Capitalization, Colons**

    We looked in the paper to see if good morning america was on at 7 0 0 or 8 0 0.

* **Quotation Marks, Commas (To Set Off a Speaker's Words)**

    My little sister can read a stop sign bragged Matthew.

* **Forms of Verbs, Apostrophes (In Contractions)**

    Sue and Beth is going to the movies, and theyll come right home.

* **Apostrophes (To Show Ownership),
   Commas (Between Describing Words)**

    Steves family had a long bumpy flight over the mountains.

Proofreading SENTENCES

Science and Inventions

* **Colons, Commas (In a Compound Sentence), Capitalization**

   Our assembly will begin at 1 3 0 and the speaker will tell us about some of Benjamin franklin's inventions.

* **Capitalization, Forms of Verbs**

   In 1931 the empire state building is the tallest building in the world.

* **Apostrophes (In Contractions), Commas (To Keep Numbers Clear)**

   I wouldnt want to wash the windows of the Empire State Building because its 1 2 5 0 feet tall!

* **Apostrophes (In Contractions), Run-On Sentence**

   Were lucky that vaccines have been developed many people would have died without them.

* **Hyphens (In Fractions), Capitalization**

   Mars is about one half the size of earth.

Proofreading SENTENCES

Science and Inventions

* **Capitalization, Commas (To Keep Numbers Clear), End Punctuation**

    The Sears tower is 1 4 5 4 feet tall

* **Capitalization, Forms of Adjectives**

    henry ford wanted to produce automobiles more faster than before.

* **Commas (Between Day and Year in a Date), Capitalization, Using the Right Word**

    The Concorde made it's first flights to Paris, london, and New york on November 22 1977.

* **Capitalization, End Punctuation**

    In 1957 the russians launched an orbiting satellite called *Sputnik*

* **Forms of Verbs, Commas (Between Describing Words)**

    Subways is train systems that travel through dark underground tunnels.

Science and Inventions

✳ **Apostrophes (To Show Ownership), Capitalization**

Samuel Morses great invention was the morse code.

✳ **Capitalization, Using the Right Word, End Punctuation**

did you no that a sewing machine is used to bind
books

✳ **Using the Right Word, Commas (To Keep Numbers Clear),
Run-On Sentence**

In 1879 Thomas Edison invented the lightbulb he maid
more than 1 0 0 0 inventions in his lifetime.

✳ **Capitalization, Run-On Sentence**

In 1793 Eli whitney invented the cotton gin in 1798 he
invented mass production.

✳ **Using the Right Word, Apostrophes (To Show Ownership)**

Scientists wonder if there is a whole in the earths
ozone layer.

Proofreading SENTENCES

Literature and Life

✱ Run-On Sentence, Titles

The first successful newspaper was published in 1704 it was called the Boston News-Letter.

✱ Titles, Capitalization, Periods (In Abbreviations), End Punctuation

Cat in the hat is a famous book by Dr Seuss

✱ Capitalization, Commas (In City and State), Sentence Fragments

In 1757 streetlights were installed in philadelphia pennsylvania. Easier to see at night.

✱ Quotation Marks, Capitalization, Periods (In Abbreviations)

america's first ice-cream company was founded in 1786, said Mr Thomas.

✱ Capitalization, Commas (In a Compound Sentence)

The american bald eagle was chosen as a U.S. symbol but Benjamin franklin wanted the turkey to be chosen.

Proofreading SENTENCES

Literature and Life

* **Apostrophes (In Contractions), Titles, Capitalization**

  My mom cant sing the high notes in The Star-spangled Banner, but she tries her best.

* **Titles, Apostrophes (To Show Ownership), Sentence Fragments**

  Lewis Carroll wrote Alices Adventures in Wonderland. Finished in 1865.

* **Periods (After Initials), Colons, Commas (In a Series)**

  L Frank Baum is the creator of these characters the Scarecrow the Cowardly Lion and the Tin Man.

* **Titles, Run-On Sentence, Capitalization**

  My brother reads the magazine Boy's Life it helps him in boy scouts.

* **Commas (In a Compound Sentence), Apostrophes (In Contractions)**

  Charles Schulz created *Peanuts* in 1950 and its my favorite comic strip.